ANTMEN

CARRY AWAY

MY

THOUGHTS

AS

SOON AS I

THINK

THEM

OTHER BOOKS BY STEVEN APPLEBY:

Normal Sex
Men the Truth
Miserable Families
Steven Appleby's Secret Thoughts

ANTMEN CARRY AWAY MY THOUGHTS
AS SOON AS I THINK THEM.

OF L

Steven Appleby

First published November 1997

Copyright Steven Appleby © 1997

The moral right of the author has been asserted

Bloomsbury Publishing PLC
38 Soho Square, London W1V 5DF

ISBN 0 7475 3740 2

Printed in Great Britain by St Edmundsbury Press, Suffolk

Dear Reader,

London...

Most of the drawings in this book first appeared in The Guardian — the remainder (pages 16, 59, 62, 63, 64 & 78) were published by The Sunday Telegraph.

I have re-drawn all the black and white drawings for the book in order to standardise the shapes and sizes of the drawings, and because they were originally coloured. The colour pages are exactly the pictures which appeared in the newspapers.

There was something else I wanted to say, but, er... um... ah...

Steven Appleby 7.9.97

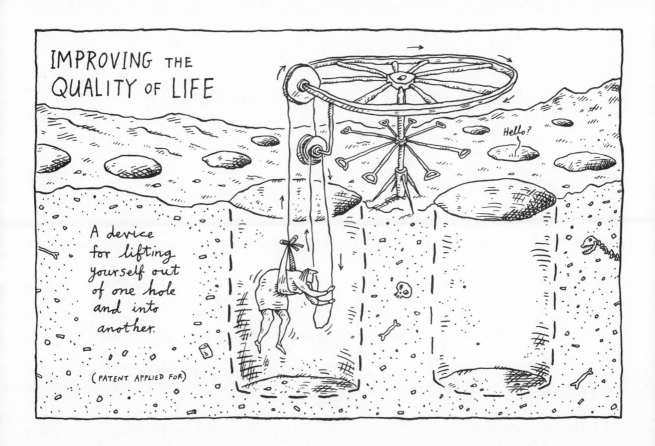

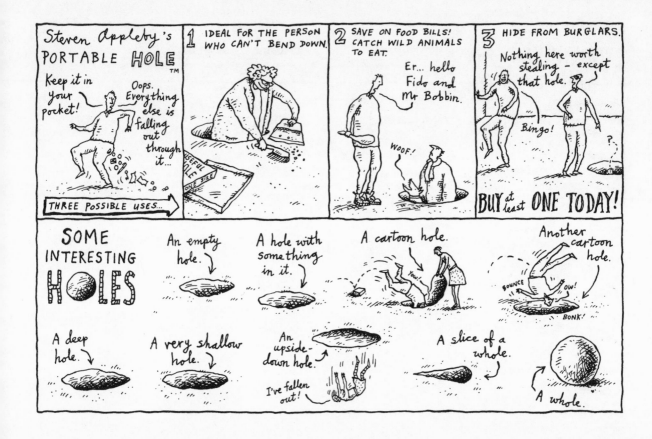

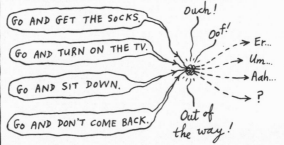

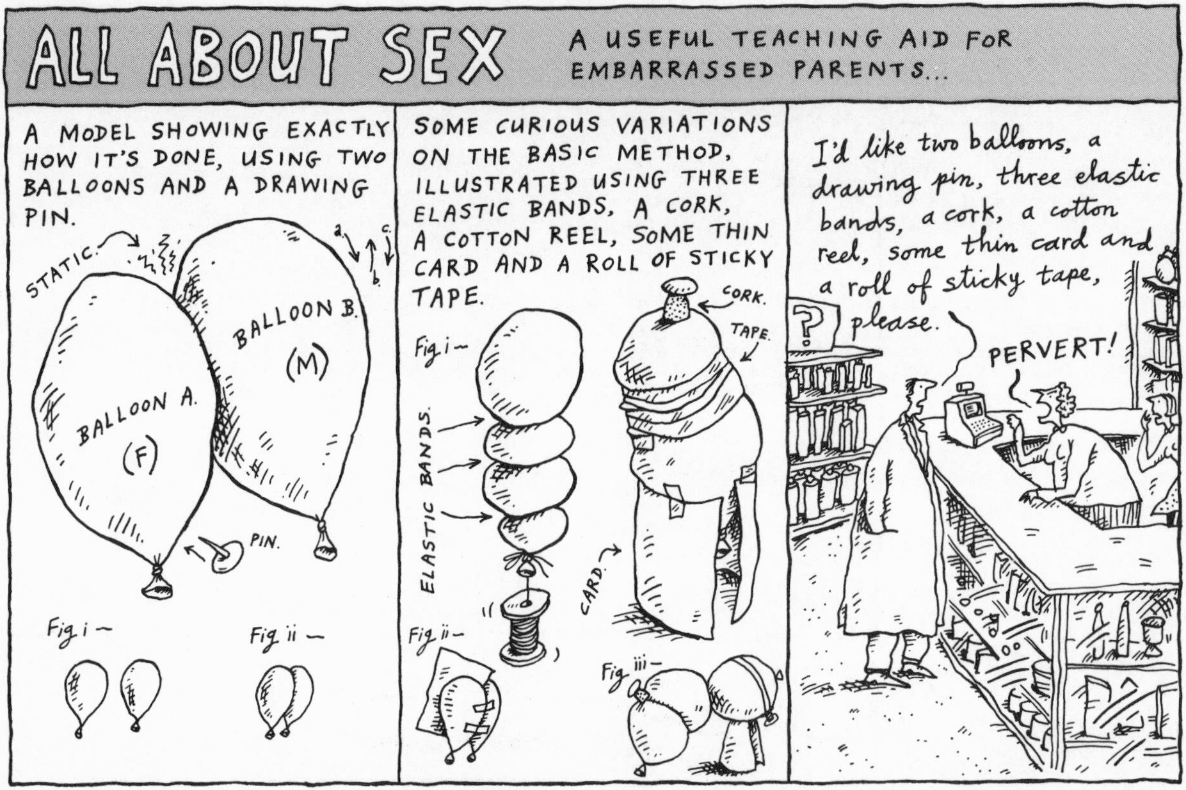
ALL ABOUT SEX
A USEFUL TEACHING AID FOR EMBARRASSED PARENTS...
A MODEL SHOWING EXACTLY HOW IT'S DONE, USING TWO BALLOONS AND A DRAWING PIN.
STATIC.
a.
b.
c.
BALLOON B.
(M)
BALLOON A.
(F)
PIN.
Fig i ~
Fig ii ~
SOME CURIOUS VARIATIONS ON THE BASIC METHOD, ILLUSTRATED USING THREE ELASTIC BANDS, A CORK, A COTTON REEL, SOME THIN CARD AND A ROLL OF STICKY TAPE.
CORK.
TAPE.
Fig i ~
ELASTIC BANDS.
CARD.
Fig ii ~
Fig iii ~
I'd like two balloons, a drawing pin, three elastic bands, a cork, a cotton reel, some thin card and a roll of sticky tape, please.
PERVERT!

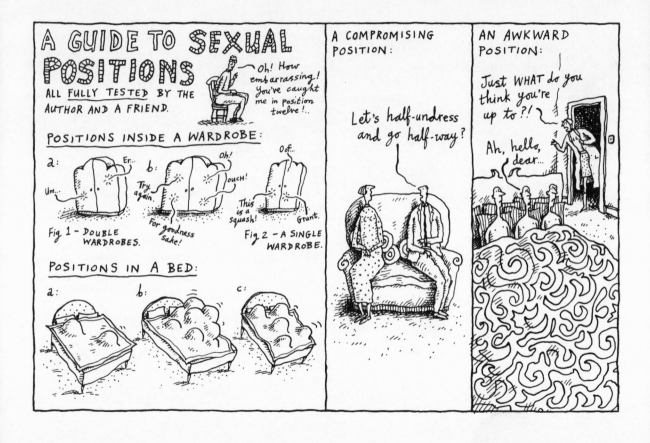

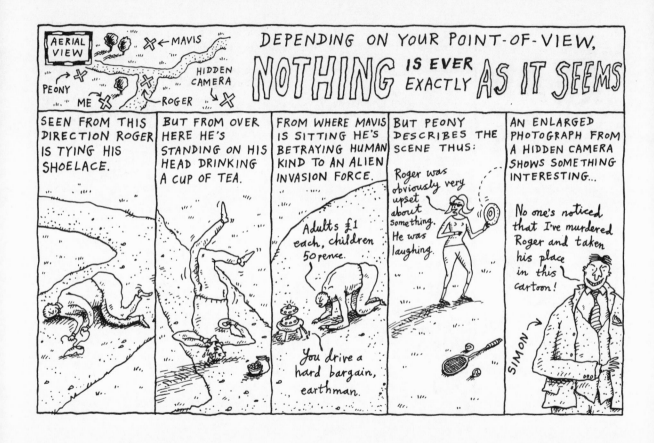

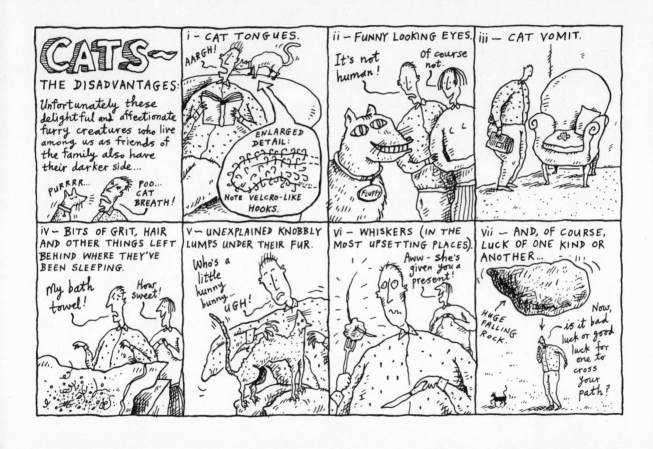

VIEWS INSIDE FISH, FROGS and OTHER THINGS...

SOME PICTURESQUE CLOUD FORMATIONS SEEN INSIDE A PLAICE.

A LOVELY SUNSET WITHIN A HALIBUT.

A DELIGHTFUL MISTY MORNING INSIDE A FROG.

THE ENTIRE UNIVERSE - VISIBLE INSIDE A TURNIP IF YOU KNOW WHERE TO LOOK.

THE RATHER DISAPPOINTING CONTENTS OF A BALLOON.

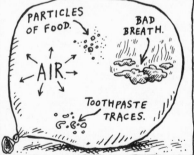

PARTICLES OF FOOD.

BAD BREATH.

AIR

TOOTHPASTE TRACES.

PET THERAPY

IT IS A WELL-KNOWN FACT THAT OWNING A PET CAN HAVE A POWERFUL CALMING AND MEDICINAL EFFECT... HERE WE SEE PETS USED TO TREAT SOME COMMON CONDITIONS:

1 — BEING BORING:

Nowadays I feel interesting compared to my pet potato, Michael.

2 — WORRY. WHY NOT ACQUIRE AN ELEPHANT TO WORRY ABOUT?

I feel better because her problems are colossal compared to mine!

NELLIE

3 — GUILT. THIS CANNIBAL HAS FOUND THAT A PET SHEEP SOLVES HIS PROBLEM.

All my guilt has gone. I can eat Deirdre without anyone minding.

4 — THE NEED TO PROCREATE. THIS LADY HAS SATISFIED HER DRIVE TO BREED BY FINDING A SMALL FURRY CREATURE TO LOVE.

Now I don't need to have children.

Aw, Mum!

UNKNOWN INVENTORS 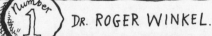 DR. ROGER WINKEL.

Eureka!

Here's Roger Winkel wearing his everlasting force-field trousers. These never wear out because the invisible field keeps them from rubbing against buttocks, legs and chairs.

Comfy.

Here's Roger again modelling trousers, socks, shoes, coat, hat, gloves and underwear made from his unique force-field fabric.

Thanks to Roger, in the future people will need only one of each item of clothing as his material never needs cleaning — dust, dirt, stains and even smells are held away by the invisible rays.

MUD
SLIPS
OFF
LEAVING
FABRIC
SPOTLESS

Washing the clothes would be a complete waste of time since water and soap powder can never physically touch them.

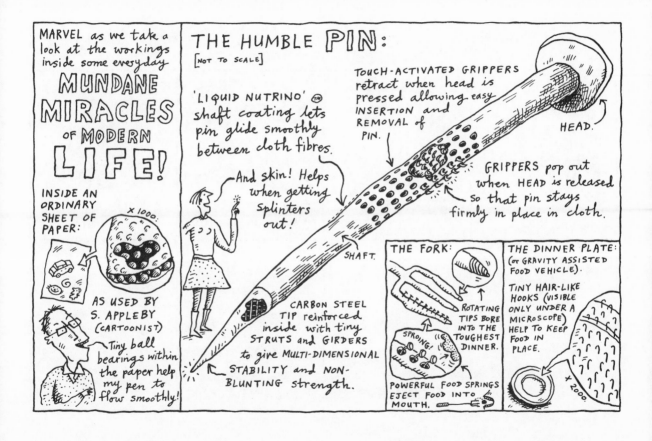

GRASPING THE UNIMAGINABLE

SOME HELPFUL WAYS TO THINK OF THE UNIVERSE...

A HANDLE.

A REFLECTION.

A SOCK THAT IS ALWAYS INSIDE-OUT.

A TANGLED BALL OF STRING.

THE BACK OF AN ENVELOPE.

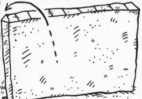

THE OTHER SIDE OF A HIGH WALL — ALONG WITH GREENER GRASS.

A VACUUM FLASK.

HOW TO ASSEMBLE THINGS

fig 1 – CHILDREN.

All things bright and beautiful...

A (SCHOOL) ASSEMBLY.

fig 2 – FROGS.

ARM 1

PIN

ARM 2

BODY

LEG 1   LEG 2

fig 4 – FLOWERS: ASSEMBLING & PLANTING.

ROOTS.

PETALS.

MIDDLE BIT.

LEAVES.

STALK.

fig 3 – POTATOES...

YOU WILL NEED:

MASH.   GLUE.   SKIN.   EYES.

One I prepared earlier.

fig 5 – HOW TO ASSEMBLE TWO OR MORE IDEAS INTO A PLAN OF ACTION.

I want his share!

So do I.

Me too. Let's take it!

fig 6 – HOW TO ASSEMBLE NUDISTS INTO A COLONY:

Oof!

Don't push!

Ouch!   Elbows in!

Careful...

Squeeze up...

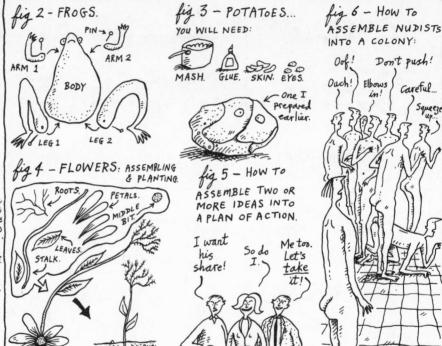

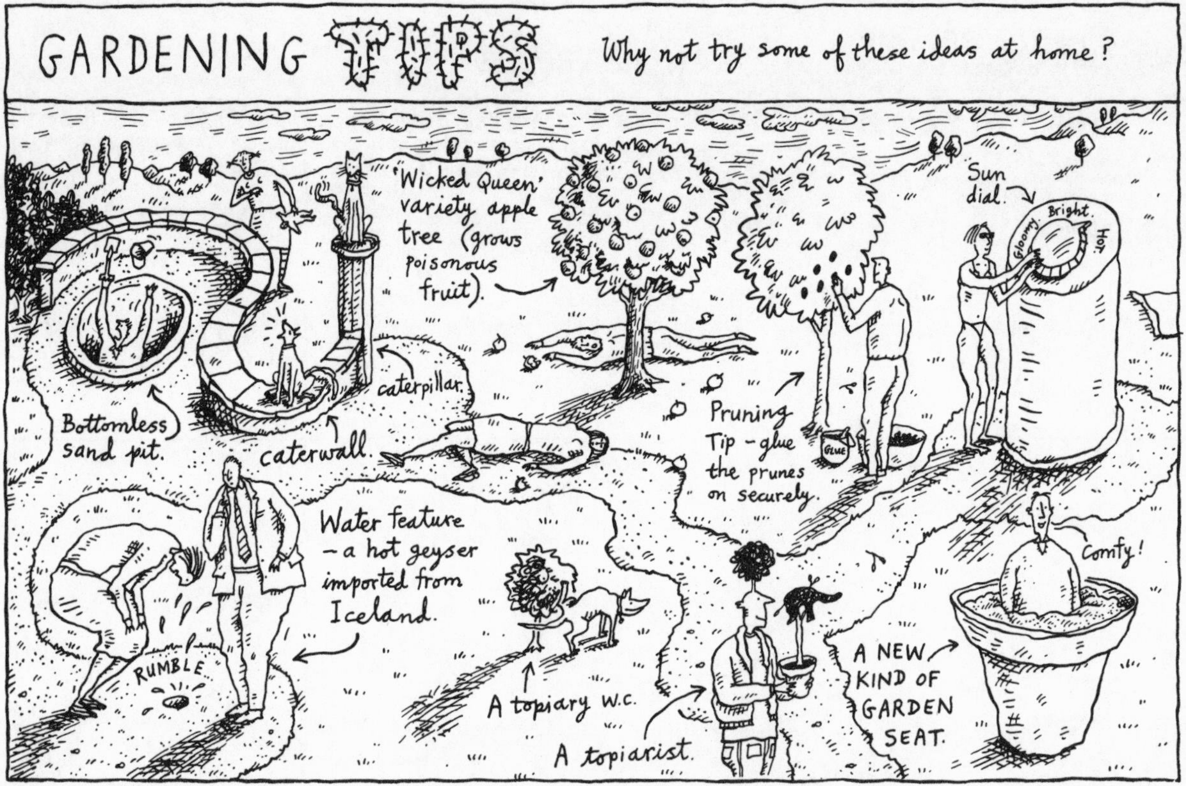

GARDENING TIPS — Why not try some of these ideas at home?

"Wicked Queen" variety apple tree (grows poisonous fruit).

caterpillar.

Sun dial.

Spooky   Bright   Hot

Bottomless sand pit.

caterwall.

Pruning Tip – glue the prunes on securely.

GLUE

Water feature – a hot geyser imported from Iceland.

RUMBLE

A topiary w.c.

A topiarist.

Comfy!

A NEW KIND OF GARDEN SEAT.

HOW TO SPOT GOOD and BAD FRUIT and VEGETABLES

SELECTED BY Steven Appleby.

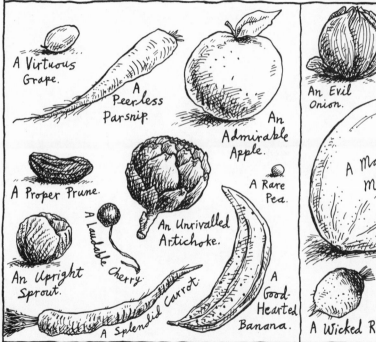

A Virtuous Grape.

A Peerless Parsnip.

An Admirable Apple.

A Proper Prune.

A Rare Pea.

An Unrivalled Artichoke.

A Laudable Cherry.

An Upright Sprout.

A Splendid Carrot.

A Good-Hearted Banana.

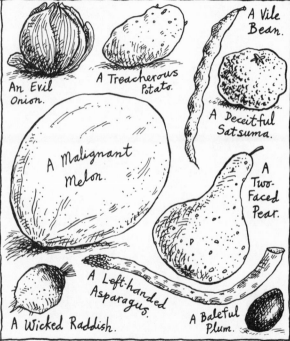

An Evil Onion.

A Treacherous Potato.

A Vile Bean.

A Deceitful Satsuma.

A Malignant Melon.

A Two-Faced Pear.

A Left-handed Asparagus.

A Wicked Raddish.

A Baleful Plum.

BUILDING BRIDGES

Let's make up...

A STURDY BRIDGE BETWEEN TWO PEOPLE OF LIKE MINDS.

Good idea.

I agree.

AN UNINSPIRED YET FUNCTIONAL BRIDGE BETWEEN MR AND MRS BOBBIN.

A RATHER RICKETY BRIDGE BETWEEN A WOMAN AND HER EX-PARTNER.

Mummy!

Daddy!

A DELIGHTFUL BUT FLIMSY, IMPRACTICAL AND UN-THOUGHT-THROUGH BRIDGE BETWEEN TWO YOUNG THINGS.

I like spinach.

Me too! Let's get married...

A BRIDGE BETWEEN AN ESTRANGED MOTHER & SON.

Darling!

Aw, Mum...

CRASH!

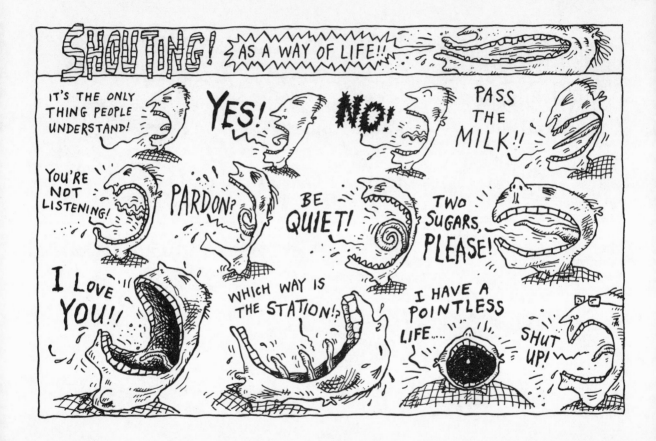

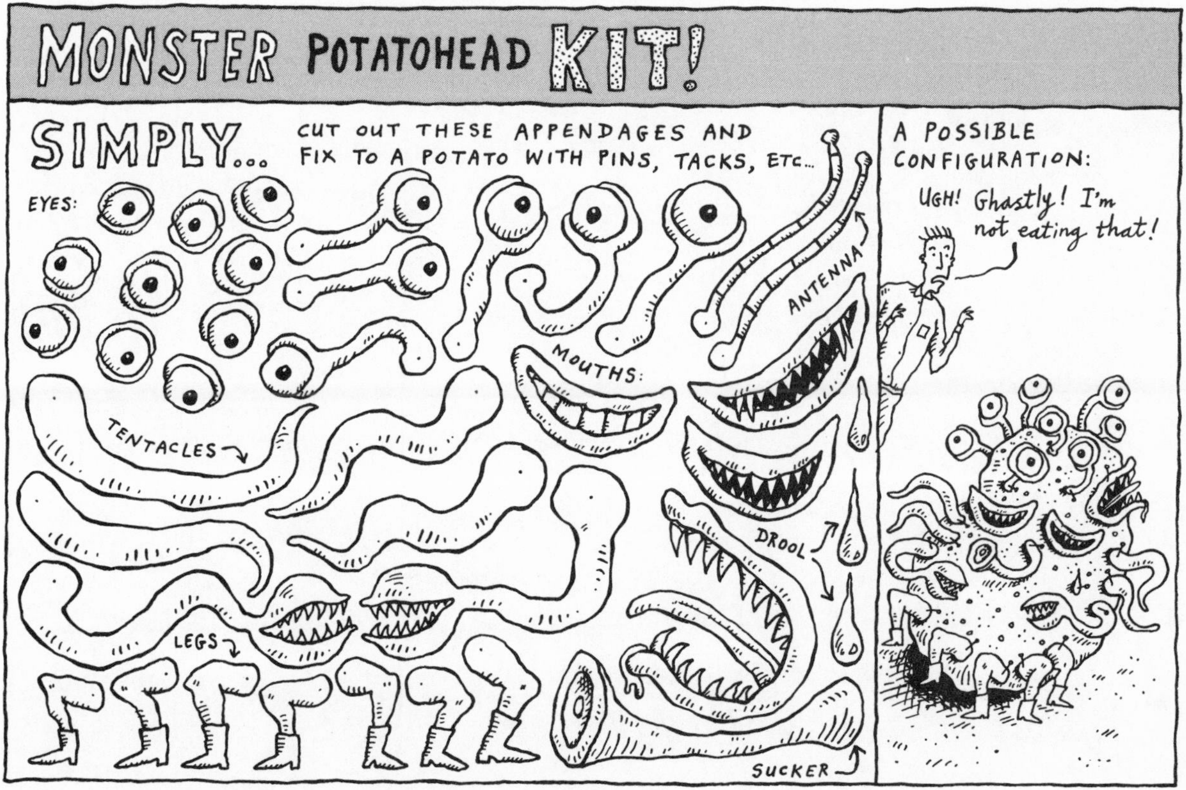
MONSTER POTATOHEAD KIT!
SIMPLY... CUT OUT THESE APPENDAGES AND FIX TO A POTATO WITH PINS, TACKS, ETC...
EYES:
ANTENNA
MOUTHS:
TENTACLES
DROOL
LEGS
SUCKER
A POSSIBLE CONFIGURATION:
UGH! Ghastly! I'm not eating that!

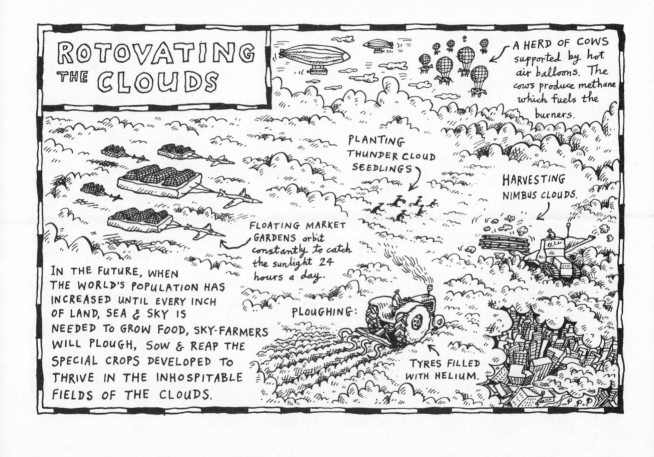

ROTOVATING THE CLOUDS

A HERD OF COWS supported by hot air balloons. The cows produce methane which fuels the burners.

PLANTING THUNDER CLOUD SEEDLINGS

HARVESTING NIMBUS CLOUDS.

FLOATING MARKET GARDENS orbit constantly to catch the sunlight 24 hours a day.

IN THE FUTURE, WHEN THE WORLD'S POPULATION HAS INCREASED UNTIL EVERY INCH OF LAND, SEA & SKY IS NEEDED TO GROW FOOD, SKY-FARMERS WILL PLOUGH, SOW & REAP THE SPECIAL CROPS DEVELOPED TO THRIVE IN THE INHOSPITABLE FIELDS OF THE CLOUDS.

PLOUGHING:

TYRES FILLED WITH HELIUM.

INSIDERS DISCOVER THAT THEY HAVE BEEN OUTSIDE ALL ALONG.

A USEFUL GUIDE TO SHOP LIFTING

WRONG!
STRAIGHT LEGS, BENT BACK.

RIGHT!
BENT LEGS, BACK STRAIGHT.

A LIGHT SHOP:

WHAT HAPPENS WHEN **YOU** DIE...

i ~ NOTHING.

Excuse me, is Heaven this way, or...

No such place, mate.

ii ~ ALL YOUR ACCUMULATED KNOWLEDGE AND EXPERIENCE IS LOST.

So none of us knows that clever little short cut to the Saver Centre?

I wish we'd asked him before it was too late.

iii ~ ALL YOUR THINGS ARE DIVIDED UP.

Do you want his collection of price tags?

Bin them.

CHARITY SHOP Collection

iv ~ SO WHY NOT SET FIRE TO YOUR BELONGINGS, SELL YOUR HOUSE AND LIVE SIMPLY IN A MOTOR HOME?

He was burning his belongings and died in the inferno.

Sad...ish.

HEY YOU! DON'T LET YOURSELF BE BURIED ALIVE!

HAVE ONE OF OUR LIFELINE™ ALARMS FITTED TO YOUR COFFIN!

This little beauty can be heard over one hundred yards away through solid rock!

Marvellous!

They're always going off. We just ignore them.

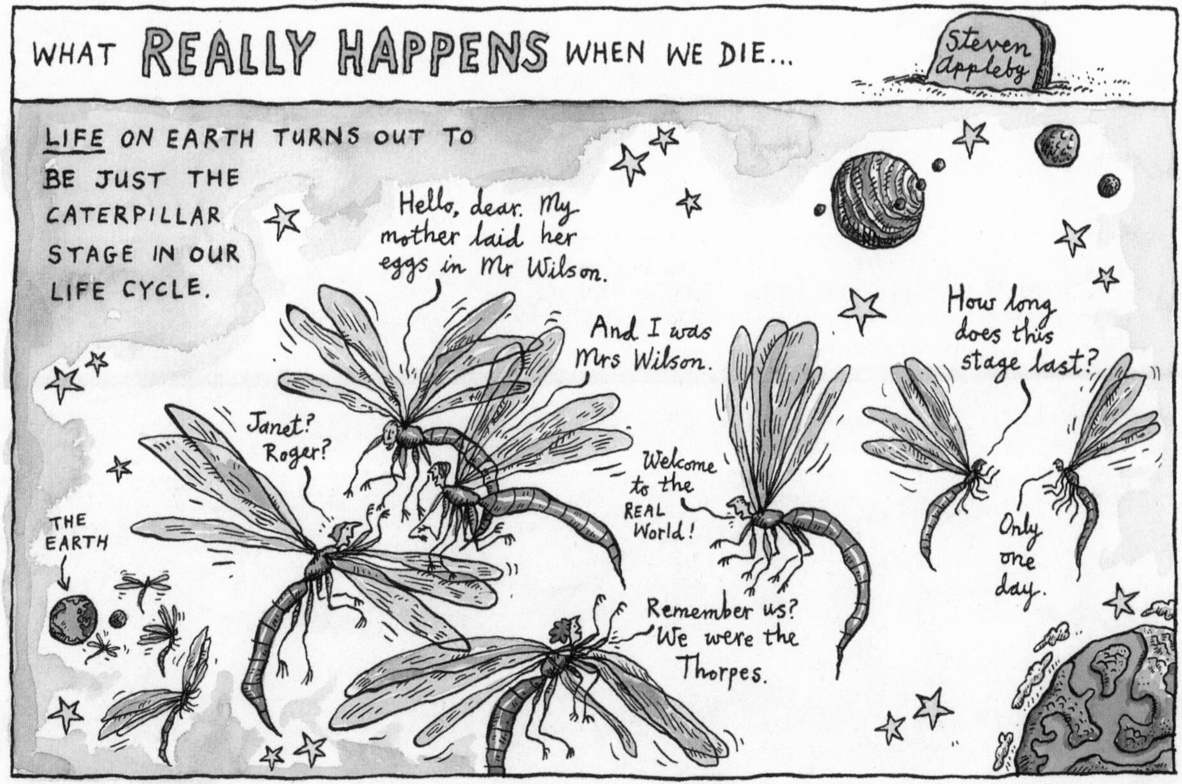
WHAT REALLY HAPPENS WHEN WE DIE...
Steven Appleby
LIFE ON EARTH TURNS OUT TO BE JUST THE CATERPILLAR STAGE IN OUR LIFE CYCLE.
Hello, dear. My mother laid her eggs in Mr Wilson.
And I was Mrs Wilson.
Janet? Roger?
Welcome to the REAL World!
How long does this stage last?
Only one day.
Remember us? We were the Thorpes.
THE EARTH

WHAT CHILDREN DO IN RESTAURANTS...
A FIRST-HAND EXPERIENCE BY
Steven Appleby.
SIT STILL FOR TEN SECONDS.
WOBBLE ON THEIR CHAIRS.
STOP THAT!
LEAN BACK ON THEIR CHAIRS.
STOP THAT!
PUT KNIVES IN THEIR MOUTHS.
Set a better example!
BANG CUTLERY.
STOP THAT!
Ratta tatta tatta tatta ta ta ta...
RATTLE CUTLERY
FOR GOODNESS SAKE!!
Tinkle tinkle tinkle tink...
PUT THEIR T-SHIRT NECK OVER THEIR NOSE.
at least he's being quiet.
MAKE MOUTH NOISE.
SHUT UP!
Whoo whoo whoo whoo whoo...
OVERFILL THEIR GLASS.
DRINK WITH NO HANDS.
SIP THEIR DRINK WITH THE CORNER OF THEIR MOUTHS.
PICK OUT THE ICE CUBES.
BLOW INTO THE NECK OF THE WINE BOTTLE.
Ssh!
Toot Toot Toot
Give it to me!
RUN THEIR FINGERS ROUND THE TOP OF THEIR GLASS.
Wheeeee!!
EAT!
Mmm...
Don't like it.
Lovely.
SLUMP DOWN IN THEIR CHAIR.
SIT UP!
GO UNDER THE TABLE.
Come out!
RUN ABOUT.
Other people are trying to eat their dinner!!
WIPE THEIR HANDS ON THEIR CLOTHES.
How Disgusting!
GO TO THE TOILET.
This is your sixth visit!
GET SENT TO SIT IN THE CAR.
Let's give coffee a miss.

MONSTERLAND!
by Steven Appleby.
Alfie learns that the monster has 12 stomachs, each specialising in digesting a particular bit of him.
YUM! MY FAVOURITE!
Disgusting.
SLAVER
HEADS & BRAINS
KNEES
STRING
TEETH
SWORDS & SCABBARDS
PACKED LUNCH (including tin).
MARBLES
SHOES & SOCKS
BALLOONS
ODD BITS OF LEGO
BONES & OTHER CRUNCHY PARTS
EVERYTHING ELSE...

HAVING A CHILD MAKES YOU REALISE...

a Steven
Appleby
announcement
™

...HOW SHORT A CHILD IS.

So tiny!

Da!

...HOW SHORT CHILDHOOD IS.

Got any condoms I can borrow, Dad?

SKUNK

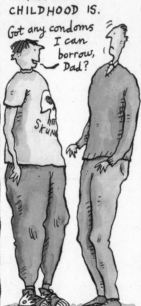

...HOW SHORT YOU ARE.

Yo, Dad!

I'M IN A BAND

PENSION

...HOW SHORT LIFE IS.

Hi Dad! We brought the kids to your deathbed. They're so TINY!

A CELEBRATION.
Seventeen nudists throw imaginary hats in the air.

Steven Appleby.

THE AMAZING WAY OSMOSIS WORKS...
I've got a terrible headache...
Perhaps it will leave my head and go into this chest of drawers by osmosis.
Nope – I've still got the headache.
EMPTY!

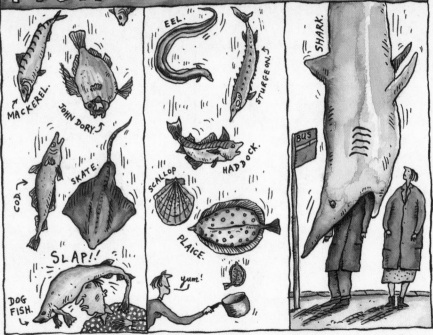

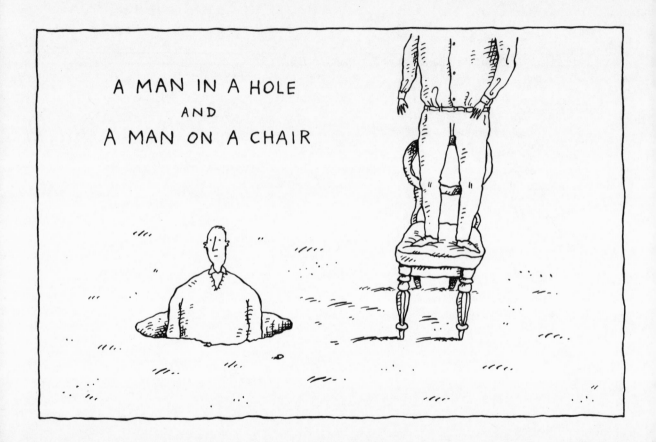

Help! Help! Help! Help!

PERHAPS THIS FRUITBOWL IS A METAPHOR FOR LIFE AND DEATH?

Yow! TOOT!

DOES THIS FALLING TEAPOT SIGNIFY SOMETHING IMPORTANT?

Yip! Yap! Woof!

THESE THREE DOGS DON'T REPRESENT ANYTHING AT ALL.

THIS TITLE BOX IS IN THE WRONG PLACE.

Could there be some deep significance to it??

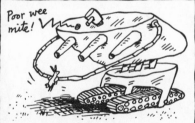

Poor wee mite!

A DEATH ROBOT FROM PLANET 47c HELPS A SICK BUNNY RABBIT — WHICH MUST SYMBOLISE AN ETERNAL TRUTH.

HOWEVER, THE UNIVERSAL FISHERMAN — WAITING FOREVER AS THE TROUT OF INDECISION CIRCLES THE HOOK OF DESTINY — IS OBVIOUSLY UTTER RUBBISH!

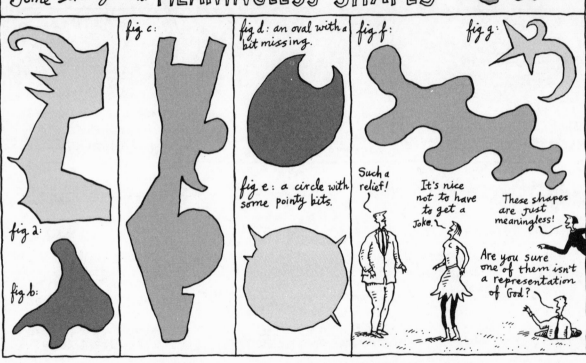

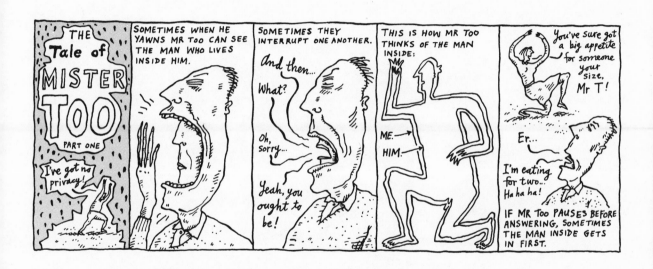

UNKNOWN INVENTORS
Number 2
THE INVENTOR WHO GAVE UP AFTER THE 'YO'.
Well, it goes down alright...
TOTALLY STATIONARY

SOME RANDOM WORDS & MARKS WHICH HAPPEN TO RESEMBLE A CARTOON

EVERY TIME WE TURN ON A LIGHT SWITCH THE LIGHT COMES ON.

Even if you have your eyes closed.

CLICK!

THIS IS CALLED A COINCIDENCE.

PEOPLE USUALLY THINK OF A COINCIDENCE AS A RARE EVENT, SUCH AS A CHANCE MEETING...

Well I never! You look just like me... and you're saying the same things!

OR A VEGETABLE WHICH HAPPENS TO LOOK LIKE A HUMAN PART.

Yummy in a pie!

IN FACT, COINCIDENCES ARE EXTREMELY COMMON INDEED.

Every time I open a boiled egg, there's a yoke inside!

remark-able...

THE CORRECT FUNCTIONING OF EVERYDAY THINGS IS BASED ON COINCIDENCE.

Coincidentally, air passing over the wings is causing lift — as it did yesterday. Luckily...

HERE WE SEE THE RESULT OF TOO FEW COINCIDENCES:

Is this the bathroom, Mum?

Not today, dear. And I'm not your mother.

WITHOUT COINCIDENCES THE WORLD WOULD BE A CHAOTIC AND UNPREDICTABLE PLACE.

Toot!

THIS IS AN ELEPHANT.

Steven Appleby

GIVES SOME UNSOLICITED ADVICE

Always finish a course of antibiotics!

GASP! How true!

SEND ME ALL YOUR MONEY!

What a good idea.

I feel lighter of heart just thinking of it.

DON'T ANSWER YOUR DOOR TO STRANGLERS.

Do you mean 'strangers'?

Not necessarily. The strangler might be someone you know.

GO TO THE SHOP **RIGHT NOW** AND BUY SOME MILK.

It's really annoying to run out. Hmm... Better get a pint in...

ALWAYS ANSWER A QUESTION BY ASKING A HARDER ONE.

Do you know the way to the supermarket?

Do you know how to dismantle a train?

PERSON A   PERSON B

ALWAYS READ THIS CARTOON!

Next week there might be a SPECIAL OFFER!

Or a **FREE GIFT!!**

Perhaps some underwear.

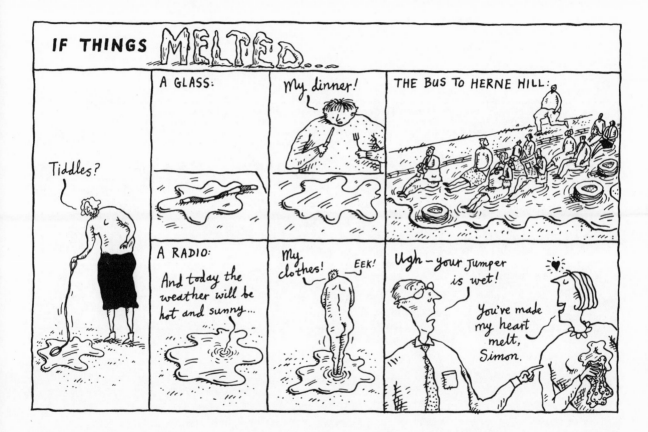

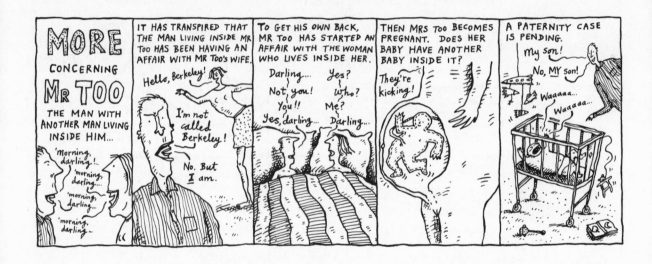

What WORTHLESS, POINTLESS & ANNOYING lives FLIES lead!

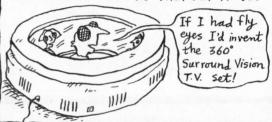

UNKNOWN INVENTORS

AN INVERTED SNOB

THIS MAN HAS INVENTED A NEW MOOD AND IS SUFFERING FROM IT.

I'm not an inventor! I'm an ARTIST!!

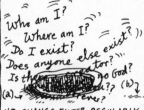

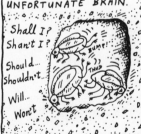

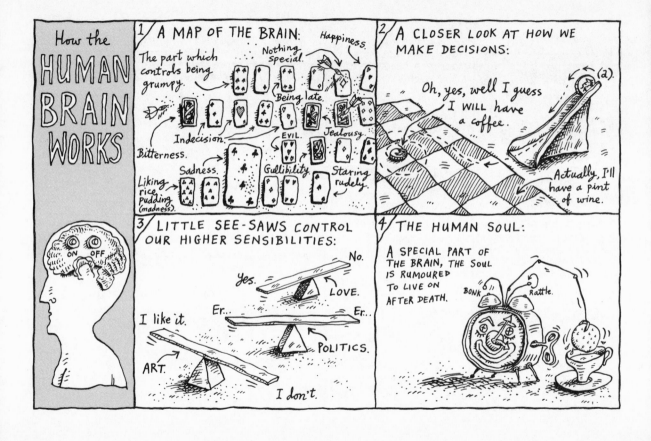

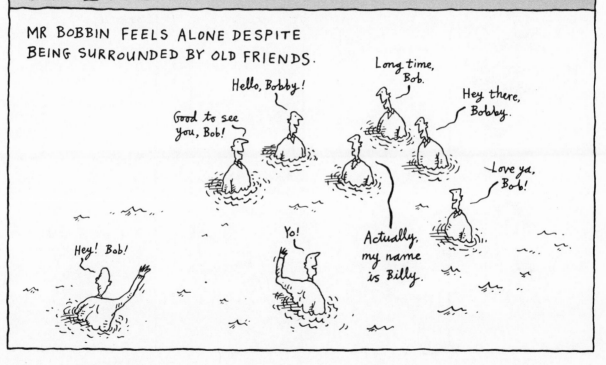

MIRACLES
OF THE
FUTURE

Some exciting predictions for the end of the century...

ADVANCES IN FOOD TECHNOLOGY WILL GIVE US HOT DRINKS AS A GAS.

But this coffee is cold!

SNOW

DIGITISED TAKE-AWAY MEALS WILL BE DELIVERED BY TELEPHONE.

SPLAT!

TALKING HAIRSTYLES WILL BE A BRIEF FAD.

Who am I?

...and why?

2-D GLASSES WILL LET US SEE REAL LIFE FLAT — JUST LIKE ON T.V.

I'm leaving you!

Wow!

Must watch next week!

EAST AND WEST WILL COLLABORATE ON SPACE TRAVEL...

Let's find a planet to use up.

Da...

...AND A NEW CONSTELLATION WILL BE DISCOVERED.

GO BACK

FINALLY, SOME OF EARTH'S LARGER MAMMALS WILL BECOME EXTINCT...

Me?

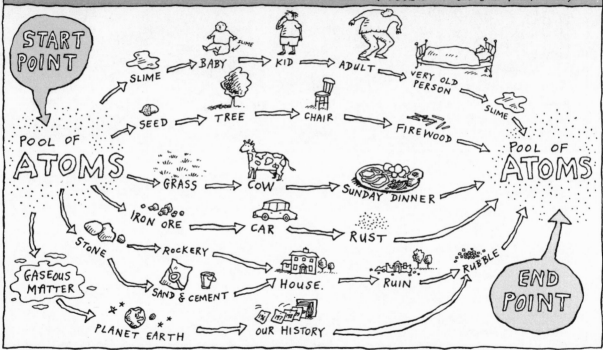

MY DRAWING
HAND.

AFTERTHOUGHT!

Some useful information concerning
the drawings in this book.

INCREDIBLE BUT TRUE!

IT CAN NOW BE REVEALED THAT THE CHARACTERS IN THIS BOOK COME COMPLETE WITH **REAL BODILY FUNCTIONS!**

STOCK FEMALE CHARACTER:

Oops... I've just broken wind!

Poo!

TOOT!

STOCK MALE CHARACTER:

Well, I've got B.O., dandruff and I pick my nose.

I CERTAINLY won't be in another drawing with you!

UGH.

POORLY DRAWN CAT:

I've got bad breath - just like a flesh and blood cat.

NOW, THIS IS A CHARACTER WORTH... OH. HE'S GONE OFF TO USE THE LAVATORY!

Excuse me!

A QUALITY CONTROL PLEDGE!

1 – STEVEN APPLEBY CARTOONS CONTAIN ONLY THE VERY BEST QUALITY CHARACTERS:

FUNNY & INTERESTING CHARACTER.

Woof! Woof!

Oh... er... um... Yow!

INARTICULATE CHARACTER.

REJECT!

2 – THEY ARE GUARANTEED FREE OF OBSCURE AND MEANINGLESS PUNCHLINES...

A hinged walrus! Ha ha...

Ho ho! How pertinent. So true.

Spot on! Hee hee...

ONLY GRADE ONE CARTOON INKS & COLOURS ARE USED.

PLEASE NOTE: OPINIONS EXPRESSED BY THE CHARACTERS ARE <u>NOT</u> NECESSARILY THOSE OF THE CREATOR!

S. Appleby stinks!

He's just not funny.

AND HERE IS YOUR **FREE GIFT!**

A LONGER FUTURE

Just cut out these EXTRA LONG and UNBROKEN Life Lines and GLUE onto your palms. Now start planning your 100th birthday party!